Health and Safety Executive

Health and safety series booklet HSR25

Memorandum of guidance on the Electricity at Work Regulations 1989

HSE BOOKS

© *Crown copyright 1989*
Applications for reproduction should be made in writing to:
Copyright Unit, Her Majesty's Stationery Office,
St Clements House, 2-16 Colegate, Norwich NR3 1BQ

First published in 1989
Reprinted 1990 (twice), 1993, 1998 (with amendments), 1998,
1999, 2000 (twice)

ISBN 0 7176 1602 9

This guidance is issued by the Health and Safety Executive. Following the guidance is not compulsory and you are free to take other action. But if you do follow the guidance you will normally be doing enough to comply with the law. Health and safety inspectors seek to secure compliance with the law and may refer to this guidance as illustrating good practice.

Contents

Foreword

This booklet is one of three that set out the Electricity at Work Regulations 1989 and give guidance on them. The two other booklets relate specifically to mines and to quarries respectively.

This booklet is relevant to all work activities and premises except mines and quarries, certain offshore installations and certain ships.

After the introduction, the text of each regulation is given in italics followed by guidance on that regulation. Regulations 17 to 28 (which apply to mines only) are omitted as are parts of regulation 2 which interpret terms found only in regulations 17 to 28.

Introduction

1   The Electricity at Work Regulations 1989 (the Regulations)* come into force on 1 April 1990. The purpose of the Regulations is to require precautions to be taken against the risk of death or personal injury from electricity in work activities. The full text of the Regulations, which includes those parts relevant to the mining industries, is set out in Statutory Instrument 1989 No 635 available from HMSO.

2   The Regulations are made under the Health and Safety at Work etc Act 1974 (HSW Act). The HSW Act imposes duties principally on employers, the self-employed and on employees including certain classes of trainees. The Regulations impose duties on persons (referred to in this Memorandum as 'duty holders') in respect of **systems**, **electrical equipment** and **conductors** and in respect of work activities on or near electrical equipment. (The words in **bold** are defined in regulation 2). The duties are in addition to those imposed by the HSW Act.

3   The guidance is intended to assist these duty holders in meeting the requirements of the Regulations. It will be of interest and practical help primarily to engineers (including those involved in the design, construction, operation or maintenance of electrical systems and equipment), technicians and their managers. It sets out the Regulations and gives technical and legal guidance on the Regulations except as they apply to mines or quarries. While it reflects the Health and Safety Executive's (HSE's) view of the meaning of terms used in the Regulations only the Courts can provide a binding interpretation. The purpose of this Memorandum is to amplify the nature of the precautions in general terms so as to help in the achievement of high standards of electrical safety in compliance with the duties imposed. However, for detailed advice reference must be made elsewhere and some relevant sources of information available at the time of writing are made throughout the Memorandum.

4   When those who design, construct, operate or maintain electrical installations and equipment need advice they should refer to appropriate guidance, such as may be found in national, international, reputable foreign and harmonised or industry standards and codes of practice or HSE guidance, or they should seek expert advice. Only those who have both the knowledge and the experience to make the right judgements and decisions and the necessary skill and ability to carry them into effect should undertake work subject to these Regulations. A little knowledge is often sufficient to make electrical equipment function but a much higher level of knowledge and experience is usually needed to ensure safety.

5   Because the Regulations state principles of electrical safety in a form which may be applied to any electrical equipment and any work activity having a bearing on electrical safety, they apply to all *electrical systems* and equipment (as defined) whenever manufactured, purchased, installed or taken into use even if its manufacture or installation pre-dates the Regulations. Where electrical equipment pre-dates the Regulations this does not of itself mean that the continued use of the equipment would be in contravention of the Regulations. For example, much of the equipment to which the Regulations apply may have been made to a standard, such as a British Standard, which has since been modified or superseded. It is likely to be reasonably practicable to replace it with equipment made to a more recent standard when, but only when, it becomes unsafe or falls due for replacement for other than safety

*As they apply to places of work other than mines and quarries.

reasons, whichever occurs sooner. Equally, fixed installations to which the IEE Wiring Regulations are relevant may have been installed in accordance with an earlier edition, now superseded but then current; that, in itself, does not mean that the installation does not comply with the 1989 Regulations.

6   Advice on the application of the Regulations in particular circumstances can be obtained from local offices of the appropriate Inspectorate.

The Institution of Electrical Engineers Requirements for Electrical Installations (the IEE Wiring Regulations)

7   The Institution of Electrical Engineers Requirements for Electrical Installations (the IEE Wiring Regulations)★ are non-statutory regulations. The IEE Regulations also have the status of a British Standard BS 7671: 1992 Requirements for Electrical Installations. They "relate principally to the design, selection, erection, inspection and testing of electrical installations, whether permanent or temporary, in and about buildings generally and to agricultural and horticultural premises, construction sites and caravans and their sites". The IEE Wiring Regulations is a code of practice which is widely recognised and accepted in the UK and compliance with them is likely to achieve compliance with relevant aspects of the 1989 Regulations.

8   There are however many types of system, equipment and hazard to which the IEE Wiring Regulations are not applicable; for example, certain installations at mines and quarries, equipment on vehicles, systems for public electricity supply and explosion protection. Furthermore, the IEE Wiring Regulations apply only to installations operating at up to 1000 volts a.c..

9   Installations to which the IEE Wiring Regulations are relevant may have been installed in accordance with an earlier edition, now superseded but then current. That, in itself, would not mean that the installation would fail to comply with the 1989 Regulations.

Other, Statutory Regulations

10   The Electricity Supply Regulations 1988 (Statutory Instrument No 1988/1057) impose requirements regarding the installation and use of electric lines and apparatus of suppliers of electricity including provisions for connections with earth. These Regulations are administered by the Engineering Inspectorate of the Department of Trade and Industry and may impose requirements which are in addition to those of the Electricity at Work Regulations.

Other sources of guidance

11   Guidance notes and other publications issued by HSE from time to time give detailed advice on such matters as, design of certain equipment, safe working practices, maintenance and repair of equipment, and installation practice for particular environments. A list of some of these is given in Appendix 1.

12   There exist many codes of practice written by standards-making authorities, trade associations and other bodies setting out standards and procedures applicable to particular industries, processes or hazards. Such

★Obtainable from the Institution of Electrical Engineers, PO Box 96, Stevenage, Herts, SG1 2SD.

codes may provide useful, detailed expansion of the guidance given in this booklet but it must be borne in mind how and by whom these codes have been drawn up. A list of some of these is given in Appendix 2.

European Directives

13 Purchasers and users of electrical equipment should be aware that Member States of the EEC, and enforcing authorities such as HSE within Member States, are obliged* to accept for health and safety purposes equipment which conforms to certain Directives made under Article 100 of the Treaty of Rome. Further information about these Directives can be obtained from HSE.

*Subject to a procedure for appeal.

Regulation 1

Regulation 1

Citation and commencement

These Regulations may be cited as the Electricity at Work Regulations 1989 and shall come into force on 1st April 1990.

Regulation 2

Regulation

Interpretation

(1) In these Regulations, unless the context otherwise requires -

*"circuit conductor" means any **conductor** in a **system** which is intended to carry electric current in normal conditions, or to be energised in normal conditions, and includes a combined neutral and earth conductor, but does not include a **conductor** provided solely to perform a protective function by connection to earth or other reference point;*

*"conductor" means a **conductor** of electrical energy;*

*"danger" means risk of **injury**;*

"electrical equipment" includes anything used, intended to be used or installed for use, to generate, provide, transmit, transform, rectify, convert, conduct, distribute, control, store, measure or use electrical energy;

"injury" means death or personal injury from electric shock, electric burn, electrical explosion or arcing, or from fire or explosion initiated by electrical energy, where any such death or injury is associated with the generation, provision, transmission, transformation, rectification, conversion, conduction, distribution, control, storage, measurement or use of electrical energy;

*"system" means an electrical system in which all the **electrical equipment** is, or may be, electrically connected to a common source of electrical energy, and includes such source and such equipment.*

Guidance

1   Words and phrases which are in **bold** type in the text of the regulation preceding the guidance on each regulation are those which have been assigned a special meaning by being defined in regulation 2.

Systems

2   The term 'system' includes all the constituent parts of a system, eg conductors and electrical equipment in it, and is not a reference solely to the functional circuit as a whole. It follows that something required of a system is required both of the system as a whole and of the equipment and conductors in it.

3   The definition refers to electrical systems. In the case of each system this will include all of the electrical equipment connected together and the various electrical energy sources in that system. In the case of transformers, even though there may be galvanic separation between the various windings of the transformers, where the energy is transmitted through these from one part of the electrical system to another, the transformer and all of its windings are part of the same system.

4   The definition of 'system' includes equipment which, although not energised, may be electrically connected to a common source of electrical energy. Equipment which is readily capable of being made live by a system is therefore considered to be part of that system. For example, a lighting circuit which has been disconnected from its source of electrical energy by means of removable links or fuses is still part of that system and so is such a circuit

2

4

which has been switched off even though the switch might be a double pole switch.

5   Equipment which is in any way connected to a source of electrical energy, eg a test instrument containing a source and the equipment containing or connected to that source becomes part of a system and the Regulations apply to that system. Electrical equipment which is not connected, and cannot be readily connected, to a source of electrical energy is not part of a system. Protective conductors, if they are connected to a source, are part of that system.

6   The reference in the definition to a common source of electrical energy does not exclude systems fed by several generators or transformers. The word 'common' is included in the definition so that completely independent electrical installations are regarded as separate systems. If however they are electrically connected in any way they are part of the same system for the purposes of the Regulations, even though this may mean that in some cases the system may be an extensive electrical network covering large geographical areas over which several or even many persons have control of various parts. In such cases the Regulations place duties on these persons only in respect of those provisions of the Regulations which relate to matters which are within their control (see regulation 3).

7   Self-contained portable systems such as portable generating sets are electrical systems for the purpose of the Regulations as are transportable systems and systems on vehicles etc.

Electrical equipment

8   'Electrical equipment' as defined in the Regulations includes every type of electrical equipment from for example a 400 kV overhead line to a battery-powered hand lamp. It is appropriate for the Regulations to apply even at the very lowest end of the voltage or power spectrum because the Regulations are concerned with for example explosion risks which may be caused by very low levels of energy igniting flammable gases even though there may be no risk of electric shock or burn. Thus no voltage limits appear in the Regulations. The criteria of application is the test as to whether 'danger' (as defined) may arise.

Electrical equipment (as defined) includes conductors used to distribute electrical energy such as cables, wires and leads and those used in the transmission at high voltage of bulk electrical energy, as in the national grid.

Conductors

9   Regulation 2 defines a conductor as 'a conductor of electrical energy'. This means any material which is capable of conducting electricity (electricity is synonymous with electrical energy) and therefore includes both metals and all other conducting materials. The definition is not limited to conductors intended to carry current and so includes, for example, metal structures, salt water, ionised gases and conducting particles. The conductance of most materials varies with parameters such as temperature; eg glass is conducting when molten (and is then a conductor as defined) whereas in its normal, solid, state it is a good insulator and finds many applications as such. For the purposes of the Regulations, while such materials conduct electricity, they are 'conductors'.

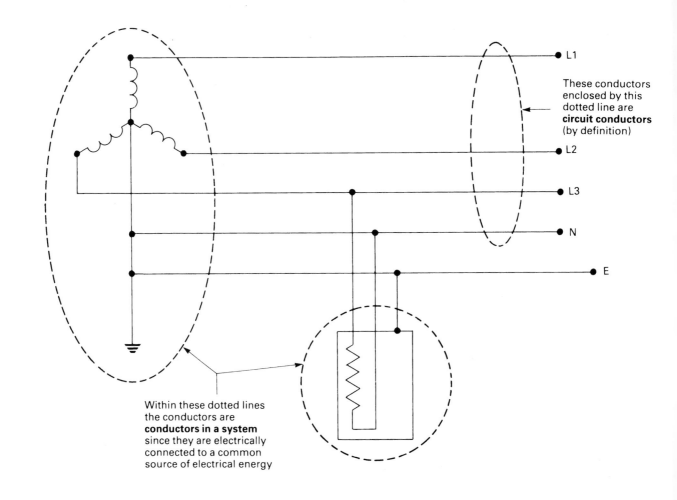

These conductors enclosed by this dotted line are **circuit conductors** (by definition)

Within these dotted lines the conductors are **conductors in a system** since they are electrically connected to a common source of electrical energy

3 Phase system – separate neutral and earth

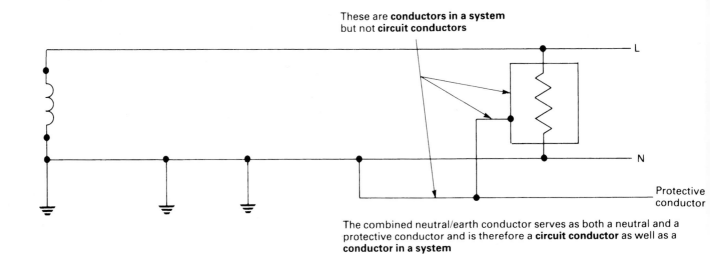

These are **conductors in a system** but not **circuit conductors**

The combined neutral/earth conductor serves as both a neutral and a protective conductor and is therefore a **circuit conductor** as well as a **conductor in a system**

System including both combined and separate neutral and earth conductors (single phase only shown)

Figure 1 Types of conductor

Circuit conductor

10   This definition is used in regulations 8 and 9 only. It distinguishes from all other conductors those conductors whose normal function is to carry load current or to be energised. (See Fig 1.)

Danger

11   The Regulations use the two defined terms, 'danger' and 'injury'. 'Danger' is defined as 'risk of *injury*'. 'Injury' is defined in terms of certain classes of potential harm to persons.

12   Where the term 'prevent danger' is used it should therefore be read as "prevent the risk of *injury*".

13   The Regulations make requirements to 'prevent danger' or 'prevent injury' - or in the case of regulation 16 - "to prevent danger or, where appropriate, injury". The purpose of the distinction between 'injury' and 'danger' is to accommodate those circumstances when persons must work on or so near live equipment that there is a risk of 'injury', ie where 'danger' is present and cannot be prevented. In these circumstances under regulation 14, danger may be present but injury must be prevented.

14   The type of injuries with which the Regulations are concerned are detailed in the definition of 'injury' in the regulation (see paragraphs 16 and 17). The scope of the Regulations does not include consequential dangers such as crushing injuries caused by a machine going out of control following an electrical malfunction. Such other dangers are subject to other legal requirements under for example the HSW Act, the Factories Act 1961 and the Offices Shops and Railway Premises Act 1963.

15   If no danger arises from a particular system, item of electrical equipment or conductor and will not arise, then the Regulations, although applying to it, do not require any precautions to be taken. However, in order for there to be no danger, there would have to be no risk of electric shock, electric burn, fire, arcing or explosion.

Injury

16   The purpose of the Regulations is to prevent death or personal injury to any person from electrical causes in connection with work activities.

17   'Injury' means death or injury to persons from:

(a)   electric shock;

(b)   electric burn;

(c)   fires of electrical origin;

(d)   electric arcing; or

(e)   explosions initiated or caused by electricity.

(a)   *Electric shock*

18   The human body responds in several ways to electrical current flowing through it. The sensation of shock is only one such effect and this can be extremely painful. When a shock is received, the electric current may take

multiple paths through the body and its intensity at any one point its difficult or impossible to predict. The passage of electric current may cause muscular contractions, respiratory failure, fibrillation of the heart, cardiac arrest or injury from internal burns. Any of these can be fatal.

19 The nature and severity of injury depends upon the magnitude, duration and path of the current through the body and, in the case of alternating current, on its frequency. It is not possible to identify precise thresholds for the existence of hazard because a judgement has to be made in each case taking all the circumstances into account such as body weight, physical condition of the victim and so forth. Nevertheless, a guide to the sort of current magnitudes which mark the occurrence of various dangerous effects is given in the International Electrotechnical Commissions publication IEC 479 (BS PD 6519). Quite low currents, of the order of only a few milliamps, can cause fatal electric shock.

20 Factors which mainly influence the likely effect of shock current are its voltage, frequency and duration and any impedance in the current path. The effects of electric shock are most acute at about the public electricity supply frequency of 50 hertz. Susceptibility to electric shock is increased if a person is in good electrical contact with earth, such as in damp or wet conditions or in conducting locations such as inside a metal tank. Hot environments where people may become damp due to perspiration or humidity, thus reducing the insulation protection offered by clothing, may present an increased risk from electric shock.

21 The variability of conditions makes it impossible to specify a voltage which is guaranteed to be safe in all situations. The risk of injury from electric shock in any situation must be considered against the background of the various national and international standards and technical publications giving guidance as to the voltages and other factors which have been found by extensive experience to be safe. These documents must be interpreted carefully and with a view to the limitation of their various scopes and assumptions. However, the conventional public electricity supply voltage of 230 volts 50 hertz a.c. should always be considered as potentially fatally dangerous. Many fatal electric shock accidents have occurred from contact with conductors live at this voltage and possibly the most dangerous situation is where contact is made with conductors by each hand, current then flowing 'hand to hand' across the heart region.

22 The following documents give some guidance.

(a)   IEC Publication 479. *Effects of current passing through the human body.* (Edition 1984 or later editions);

(b)   The Institution of Electrical Engineers Requirements for Electrical Installations (the IEE Wiring Regulations), 16th Edition;

(d)   IEC Guide 105. *Principles concerning the safety of equipment electrically connected to a telecommunications network.*

(b) Electric burn

23 Electric burns are different from burns due to fire (see paragraphs 26-27), arcing (see paragraphs 28-30) or explosion (see paragraphs 31-33).

24 Electric burns are due to the heating effect caused by the passage of electric current through body tissues. They are most commonly associated

with electric shock and often occur in and on the skin layers at the point of contact with the electrical conductors which gave rise to the electric shock.

25 At high frequencies, eg radio frequencies (RF), which include microwaves, it may not even be necessary for contact to be made with live conductors for an electric burn to be received. In the case of RF, the heating is by absorption of the electromagnetic wave energy by a dielectric loss process in the body of the victim. RF burns can thus be extremely deep within the body. RF burning can occur without the sensation of shock, particularly if no contact is made with the RF conductors, and can therefore cause severe injury before the victim is aware of their occurrence. Electric burns are usually painful and very slow to heal. Permanent scarring is common.

(c) Fires of an electrical origin

26 Fires may be started by electricity in a number of ways. The principal mechanisms are:

(a) overheating of cables and electrical equipment due to overloading of conductors;

(b) leakage currents due to poor or inadequate insulation;

(c) overheating of flammable materials placed too close to electrical equipment which is otherwise operating normally; and

(d) the ignition of flammable materials by arcing or sparking of electrical equipment, including the scattering of hot particles from electrical equipment.

27 The injuries associated with fire are usually burns but may include other injuries such as smoke inhalation.

(d) Arcing

28 Arcing causes a particular type of burn injury which is distinct from other types. Arcing generates ultra violet radiation which causes damage akin to severe sunburn. Molten metal particles from the arc itself can penetrate, burn and lodge in the flesh. These effects are additional to any radiated heat damage caused by the arc.

29 On its own, ultra violet radiation can cause damage, sensitive skin and eyes are especially vulnerable to arc flash. ('Arc eye' is commonly encountered with electric arc welding if the proper precautions are not adopted.)

30 Arcing faults can occur if the energy available at a piece of electrical equipment is sufficient to maintain a conductive path through the air or insulation between two conductors which are at different potentials. Under fault flashover conditions, currents many times the nominal rating or setting of a protective device may flow before those devices operate to clear the fault. Much energy is dissipated in the arc and depending on the electrical protection, may continue long enough to inflict very serious arcing burns or to initiate a fire in periods for example as short as 0.25 second, which is not an untypical minimum time for fault clearance. Arc flashovers caused during work on live circuit conductors are likely to be particularly hazardous because the worker is likely to be very near to or even enveloped by the arc. Such cases often lead to very serious, sometimes fatal, burn injuries.

(e) Explosion

31 In this category are those injuries caused by explosions either of an electrical nature or those whose source of ignition is electrical.

32 Electrical explosions include the violent and catastrophic rupture of any electrical equipment. Switchgear, motors and power cables are liable to explode if they are subjected to excessive currents, which release violent electromagnetic forces and dissipate heat energy, or if they suffer prolonged internal arcing faults.

33 Explosions whose source of ignition is electrical include ignition of flammable vapours, gases, liquids and dusts by electric sparks, arcs or the high surface temperature of electrical equipment.

Other words used in the Regulations

Charged/live (as used in regulations 8, 13 and 14)

34 The terms 'charged' and 'live' have different meanings; they are not defined in the Regulations so they take their ordinary meaning. 'Live' means that the item in question is at a voltage, by being connected to a source of electricity for example as in normal use. 'Charged' means that the item has acquired a charge either because it is live or because it has become charged by other means such as by static or induction charging, or has retained or regained a charge due to capacitance effects even though it may be disconnected from the rest of the system.

Dead (as used in regulations 13, 14)

35 The term 'dead' is not defined in the Regulations so it takes its ordinary meaning. Thus, in the context of the Regulations, for a conductor to be 'dead' means that it is neither 'live' nor 'charged'.

Persons on whom duties are imposed by these Regulations

(1)   Except where otherwise expressly provided in these Regulations, it shall be the duty of every -

(a)   employer and self-employed person to comply with the provisions of these Regulations in so for as they relate to matters which are within his control; and

(b)   manager of a mine or quarry (within in either case the meaning of section 180 of the Mines and Quarries Act 1954[a]) to ensure that all requirements or prohibitions imposed by or under these Regulations are complied with in so far as they relate to the mine or quarry or part of a quarry of which he is the manager and to matters which are within his control.

(a)   *1954 C.70; section 180 was amended by SI 1974/2013.*

(2) It shall be the duty of every employee while at work -

(a) to co-operate with his employer so for as is necessary to enable any duty placed on that employer by the provisions of these Regulations to be complied with; and

(b) to comply with the provisions of these Regulations in so far as they relate to matters which are within his control.

Employer

1   For the purposes of the Regulations, an employer is any person or body who (a) employs one or more individuals under a contract of employment or apprenticeship; or (b) provides training under the schemes to which the HSW Act applies through the Health and Safety (Training for Employment) Regulations 1988 (Statutory Instrument No 1988/1222).

Self-employed

2   A self-employed person is an individual who works for gain or reward otherwise than under a contract of employment whether or not he employs others.

Employee

3   Regulation 3(2)(a) reiterates the duty placed on employees by section 7(b) of the HSW Act.

4   Regulation 3(2)(b) places duties on employees equivalent to those placed on employers and self-employed persons where these are matters within their control. This will include those trainees who will be considered as employees under the Regulations described in paragraph 1.

5   This arrangement recognises the level of responsibility which many employees in the electrical trades and professions are expected to take on as part of their job. The 'control' which they exercise over the electrical safety in any particular circumstances will determine to what extent they hold responsibilities under the Regulations to ensure that the Regulations are complied with.

6   A person may find himself responsible for causing danger to arise elsewhere in an electrical system, at a point beyond his own installation. This situation may arise, for example, due to unauthorised or unscheduled back feeding from his installation onto the system, or to raising the fault power level on the system above rated and agreed maximum levels due to connecting extra generation capacity, etc. Because such circumstances are 'within his control', the effect of regulation 3 is to bring responsibilities for compliance with the rest of the regulations to that person, thus making him a duty holder.

Absolute/reasonably practicable

7   Duties in some of the regulations are subject to the qualifying term 'reasonably practicable'. Where qualifying terms are absent the requirement in the regulation is said to be absolute. The meaning of reasonably practicable has been well established in law. The interpretations below are given only as a guide to duty holders.

Absolute

8   If the requirement in a regulation is 'absolute', for example if the requirement is not qualified by the words "so far as is reasonably practicable", the requirement must be met regardless of cost or any other consideration. Certain of the regulations making such absolute requirements are subject to the Defence provision of regulation 29.

Reasonably practicable

9   Someone who is required to do something 'so far as is reasonably practicable' must assess, on the one hand, the magnitude of the risks of a particular work activity or environment and, on the other hand, the costs in terms of the physical difficulty, time, trouble and expense which would be involved in taking steps to eliminate or minimise those risks. If, for example, the risks to health and safety of a particular work process are very low, and the cost or technical difficulties of taking certain steps to prevent those risks are very high, it might not be reasonably practicable to take those steps. The greater the degree of risk, the less weight that can be given to the cost of measures needed to prevent that risk.

10   In the context of the Regulations, where the risk is very often that of death, for example, from electrocution and where the nature of the precautions which can be taken are so often very simple and cheap, eg insulation, the level of duty to prevent that danger approaches that of an absolute duty.

11   The comparison does not include the financial standing of the duty holder. Furthermore, where someone is prosecuted for failing to comply with a duty 'so far as is reasonably practicable, it would be for the accused to show the court that it was not reasonably practicable for him to do more than he had in fact done to comply with the duty (section 40 of the HSW Act).

3

Regulation 4

Systems, work activities and protective equipment

*(1)   All **systems** shall at all times be of such construction as to prevent, so far as is reasonably practicable, **danger**.*

*(2)   As may be necessary to prevent **danger, all systems** shall be maintained so as to prevent, so far as is reasonably practicable, such **danger**.*

*(3)   Every work activity, including operation, use and maintenance of a **system** and work near a **system**, shall be carried out in such a manner as not to give rise, so far as is reasonably practicable, to **danger**.*

*(4)   Any equipment provided under these Regulations for the purpose of protecting persons at work on or near **electrical equipment** shall be suitable for the use for which it is provided, be maintained in a condition suitable for that use, and be properly used.*

4

1   Regulation 4 covers, in a general way, those aspects of electrical systems and equipment, and work on or near these, which are fundamental to electrical safety.

Regulation 4(1)

2   The word construction in the regulation has a wide application. It may be considered to cover the physical condition and arrangement of the components

4

of a system at any time during its life. It will include aspects such as the design of the system and the equipment comprising that system.

3   In assessing the suitability of the construction of electrical systems, consideration should be given to all likely or reasonably foreseeable conditions of actual application or use of the electrical equipment in the system. This will include the testing, commissioning, operation and maintenance of the equipment throughout the life of the system.

4   In particular, consideration should be given to:

(a) the manufacturer's assigned or other certified rating of the equipment;

(b) the likely load and fault conditions;

(c) the need for suitable electrical protective devices;

(d) the fault level at the point of supply and the ability of the equipment and the protective devices to handle likely fault conditions;

(e) any contribution to the fault level from the connected loads such as from motors;

(f) the environmental conditions which will have a bearing on the mechanical strength and protection required of the equipment;

(g) the user's requirements of the installation;

(h) the manner in which commissioning, testing and subsequent maintenance or other work may need to be carried out.

5   The safety of a system depends upon the proper selection of all the electrical equipment in the system and the proper consideration of the inter-relationship between the individual items of equipment. For example, electrical protection against overloads and earth faults etc may need to be provided in one part of a system to protect another, possibly remote part of the system. Also, where electrical energy is transformed or converted from one voltage to another, precautions should be taken to prevent danger arising from the lower voltage conductors becoming charged above their normal voltage.

Regulation 4(2)

6   Regulation 4(2) is concerned with the need for maintenance to be done in order to ensure safety of the system rather than with the activity of doing the maintenance in a safe manner (which is required by regulation 4(3)).

7   The obligation to maintain arises only if danger would otherwise result. The quality and frequency of maintenance should be sufficient to prevent danger so far as is reasonably practicable.

8   Regular inspection of equipment is an essential part of any preventive maintenance programme. Practical experience of use may indicate an adjustment to the frequency at which preventive maintenance needs to be carried out. This is a matter for the judgment of the duty holder who should seek all the information he needs to make this judgment including reference to the equipment manufacturers' guidance.

9   Records of maintenance, including test results, preferably kept throughout the working life of an electrical system will enable the condition of the

equipment and the effectiveness of maintenance policies to be monitored. Without effective monitoring duty holders cannot be certain that the requirement for maintenance has been complied with.

10   British Standard Codes of Practice offering guidance on maintenance are referred to in Appendix 2. Advice on inspection and testing of some fixed installations is given in the IEE Wiring Regulations (see Introduction and Appendix 2).

Regulation 4(3)

11   Regulation 4(3) requires that work activities of any sort, whether directly or indirectly associated with an electrical system, should be carried out in a way which, as far as is reasonably practicable, does not give rise to danger. Regulations 12 to 16 provide more specific requirements in connection with work of an electrical nature on or near electrical systems.

Work activities associated with electrical systems

12   In the case of work of an electrical nature it is preferable that the conductors be made dead before work starts. (See regulations 12, 13 and 14.) In such cases it is essential that the equipment be isolated (note that 'isolation' is defined in regulation 12(2) which will include securing by locking off etc; see also paragraph 15 under this regulation) and the conductors proved dead at the point of work before the work starts. Where a test instrument or voltage indicator is used for this purpose this device should itself be proved preferably immediately before and immediately after testing the conductors.

13   Proper safe systems of work incorporating safety isolation procedures are important for work upon equipment which is to be made dead before work starts. These are also discussed under regulations 12 and 13. Some work, such as fault finding and testing, or live jointing by the electricity supply industry, may require electrical equipment to remain enegised during the work. In these cases if there may be danger from live conductors, regulation 14 makes particular requirements and regulation 4(4) is also likely to be relevant in terms of the protective equipment which may need to be provided.

14   The operation, maintenance and testing of electrical systems and equipment should be carried out only by those persons who are competent for the particular class of work. (See also regulation 16.)

Disused electrical equipment and systems

15   Before electrical equipment is decommissioned or abandoned for any reason it should be disconnected from all sources of supply and isolated. Isolation (as defined in regulation 12(2)) requires taking effective steps to ensure that it is dead and cannot become inadvertently re-energised or charged by induction or capacitance effects. (Regulations 12, 13 and 14 are also likely to be relevant.) Suitable labels or notices to bring people's attention to the state of the equipment are likely to be necessary in preventing inadvertent re-energisation.

Other work near electrical systems

16   Regulation 4(3) is wide in its application and includes work of a non-electrical nature where there is a risk of electrical injury. A common example is excavation near to live electric power cables and work near live overhead power lines, where the risks can be severe. Advice on these matters is given in HSE guidance notes which are listed in Appendix 1. The requirements of regulation 14 must also be taken into consideration.

4

Regulation 4(4)

17 The defence (regulation 29) is available in any proceedings for an offence under this part of regulation 4.

18 The term 'protective equipment' can be of wide application but typically includes those special tools, protective clothing and insulating screening materials etc necessary to undertake work safely on live electrical equipment. The requirement for suitable precautions to prevent injury may arise under regulation 14. The regulation makes three particular requirements of the protective equipment, that it be (a) suitable for use, (b) maintained in that condition and (c) properly used.

19 Regulation 4(4) is not qualified by "so far as is reasonably practicable", nor does the regulation refer either to injury or the risk of injury, ie electrical danger. The impact of the regulation is that where protective equipment is provided in pursuance of compliance with any of the other regulations, that the equipment must conform to the requirements of regulation 4(4). Advice on safe working practices is given in HSE guidance notes; see Appendix 1. Specifications for certain types of protective equipment such as insulating gloves and floor mats are listed in Appendix 2.

Strength and capability of electrical equipment

*No **electrical equipment** shall be put into use where its strength and capability may be exceeded in such a way as may give rise to **danger**.*

1 The defence (regulation 29) is available in any proceedings for an offence under this regulation.

2 The regulation requires that before equipment is energised that the characteristics of the system to which the equipment is connected be taken into account including those pertaining under normal conditions, possible transient conditions and prospective fault conditions so that the equipment is not subjected to stress which it is not capable of handling without giving rise to danger. The effects to be considered include voltage stress and the heating and electromagnetic effects of current.

Strength and capability

3 The term 'strength and capability' of electrical equipment refers to the ability of the equipment to withstand the thermal, electromagnetic, electro-chemical or other effects of the electrical currents which might be expected to flow when the equipment is part of a system. These currents include, for example, load currents, transient overloads, fault currents, pulses of current and, for alternating current circuits, currents at various power factors and frequencies. Insulation must be effective to enable the equipment to withstand the applied voltage and any likely transient over-voltages.

4 A knowledge of the electrical specification and the tests, usually based on the requirements of national or international standards, which have been carried out either by the manufacturer or by an accredited testing organisation will assist the user in identifying the withstand properties of the equipment so that it may be selected and installed in order to comply with this regulation.

Rating

5   The strength and capability of electrical equipment is not necessarily the same as its rating. Usually the rating is that which has been assigned by the manufacturer following a number of agreed tests.

6   It is recommended that electrical equipment be used within the manufacturer's rating (continuous, intermittent or fault rating as appropriate) and in accordance with any instructions supplied with the equipment.

Fault conditions

7   In order that equipment may remain safe under prospective fault conditions it is necessary when selecting equipment to take account of the fault levels and the characteristics of the electrical protection which have been provided for the purpose of interrupting or reducing fault current (excess current protection is required by regulation 11). Most electrical equipment will be able to withstand short circuit currents safely for limited periods only. The considerations extend also to conductors and equipment provided solely for protective purposes, eg earthing conductors must be adequately rated to survive beyond fault clearance times to ensure satisfactory protective gear operation and fault clearance.

Adverse or hazardous environments

Electrical equipment which may reasonably foreseeably be exposed to -

(a)   mechanical damage;

(b)   the effects of the weather, natural hazards, temperature or pressure;

(c)   the effects of wet, dirty, dusty or corrosive conditions; or

(d)   any flammable or explosive substance, including dusts, vapours or gases,

*shall be of such construction or as necessary protected as to prevent, so far as is reasonably practicable, **danger** arising from such exposure.*

1   The regulation draws attention to the kinds of adverse conditions where danger could arise if equipment is not constructed and protected in order to withstand such exposure. The regulation requires that electrical equipment should be suitable for the environment and conditions of use to which it may reasonably foreseeably be exposed in order that danger which may arise from such exposure will be prevented so far as is reasonably practicable. The following paragraphs detail some of the conditions which electrical equipment may be subjected to. Guidance is given in these paragraphs and additional guidance may be found in the documents listed in Appendices 1 and 2. Particular attention should be paid to the IP rating (Index of Protection) of equipment (see paragraph 22). Guidance is also given under regulation 8 on the use of reduced voltage systems on construction sites and elsewhere where particularly arduous or conducting locations may exist (see paragraphs 19 to 21 under regulation 8).

Effects

2   The conditions at which the regulation is directed are those occurring naturally as well as those resulting from human activities, including the following:

16

(a) mechanical damage including impact, stress, strain, abrasion, wear, vibration and hydraulic and pneumatic pressure;

(b) effects of the weather, which include both short term (eg wind, ice and snow, lightning) and long term (eg temperature cycling) effects;

(c) natural hazards, which are those resulting from other than man's activities and include animals, trees and plants, tides and solar radiation etc;

(d) temperature and pressure;

(e) liquids which include water and other liquids and their effects, including humidity, condensation, flooding, splashing, or immersion in these, cleaning with liquids, hosing down and solvent and solvent vapour action (electrically conducting and non-conducting liquids may present different aspects of electrical danger);

(f) dirty conditions which include all contamination as a result of liquids or solids (electrically conducting and non-conducting dusts may present different aspects of electrical danger);

(g) corrosive conditions which include all chemical action and reactions and electro chemical effects;

(h) flammable substances including flammable dusts and flammable vapours;

explosive substances which include both any mixture of solids, liquids or gases which is capable of exploding and substances intended to be explosive (ie explosives).

3 In gauging the suitability of equipment for particular environments or conditions of use it is necessary to consider only those effects or exposure which are reasonably foreseeable.

Mechanical damage

4 The mechanical damage to which electrical equipment may be subjected varies considerably from one environment to another. For example, equipment designed for use in an office is unlikely to be suitable, without further protection or careful siting, in a workshop or farm environment.

5 The effects covered by regulation 6(b), (c) and (d) may also impose mechanical stresses on electrical equipment. For example, ice and wind loading, or loss of mechanical strength due to expansion and contraction resulting from temperature changes, can give rise to mechanical damage.

6 This regulation requires the mechanical protection, if necessary, of the insulation which is required under regulation 7(a). Further suitable protection in addition to basic insulation may be necessary to form the physical protection necessary to ensure the continuing integrity of basic insulation, eg conduits or a trunking for single insulated conductors or the armouring or tough external sheathing of composite or multi core electric cable.

Weather, natural hazards and extreme conditions

7 Precautions which are taken to protect a site, structure or building from natural hazards and extreme weather conditions may give some protection to the associated electrical installation, but additional protection or precautions may be necessary.

8   Extremes of temperature, pressure or humidity may result either from climatic conditions or from adjacent plant or from the use of the electrical equipment itself. Standards frequently quote the range of service conditions for electrical equipment, including temperature limits, and users should consider these when selecting equipment.

9   Guidance on the assessment of the need for lightning protection of structures and buildings etc, the design and provision of systems and their inspection, testing and maintenance is given in publications listed in Appendix 2.

Corrosive effects

10   If substances are present in the environment which either alone, in combination, or in the presence of moisture can cause accelerated corrosion of metallic enclosures or fittings, special materials or surface treatments may be necessary. In these cases it would be recommended that much of the electrical equipment, eg motors, be of a type which is totally enclosed by an appropriate corrosion resistant housing, ie not ventilated to the atmosphere.

11   Insulating materials and other materials used in electrical equipment may be affected by chemical agents or solvents. Cubicles housing electrical control equipment in hostile environments may need to be kept purged or pressurised with clean air or, in special cases, inert gas. See Appendix 2 for standards.

Dirt and dusts

12   Most industrial enclosures for electrical equipment do not resist the entry of fine dusts. Equipment should be constructed so as to resist the entry of dust and dirt where this may give rise to electrical and mechanical failures. Regular inspection and cleaning as necessary is recommended where dirt and dusts are likely to accumulate. A particular example is that of portable motor driven equipment incorporating ventilation slots which can give rise to the accumulation of potentially hazardous layers of dirt and dust.

Combustible dusts

13   In cloud form, some dusts create an explosion hazard while layers of combustible dust on electrical equipment can give rise to fire hazards. The selection, construction or installation of the equipment so exposed to combustible dust should be such as to guard against the possibility of ignition. The maximum temperature attainable on the surface of any electrical equipment where these dusts may be deposited should be considered in the selection of the equipment. The temperature of such surfaces should always be below the temperature at which any charring or smoking of dust takes place. However, appropriate dust control measures and general cleanliness which minimise the problem at source are to be preferred. See Appendix 2 for standards.

Potentially explosive atmospheres

14   If electrical equipment is used where a flammable or explosive atmosphere is likely to occur the equipment shall be so constructed that it is not liable to ignite that atmosphere.

15   The selection and installation of equipment for use in potentially explosive atmospheres should be guided by the recommendations contained in the HSE guidance and British Standards on the subject (see Appendices 1 and 2). Existing installations complying with the recommendations of earlier standards should be acceptable for continuing service, subject to proper maintenance.

16 It is recommended that the choice of electrical equipment be from that which has been certified as being in conformity with an appropriate standard.

17 Uncertified electrical equipment should not be used unless it will provide at least an equivalent level of safety to that provided by appropriately certified equipment.

18 Some manufacturing processes, for example electrostatic paint spraying, make use of the characteristics of static electricity and the design of electrical equipment needs to be such that the ignition of solvents, vapours or particulate substances is prevented. See Appendix 2 for standards.

19 The maintenance and repair of explosion protected equipment is a specialised field of work and should be undertaken only by those who have the necessary training and experience. See Appendix 2 for standards.

Other flammable substances

20 Much electrical equipment generates heat or produces sparks and this equipment should not be placed where either the heat emitted or the occurrence of sparking is likely to lead to the uncontrolled ignition of any substance.

21 The construction of the equipment should either exclude the substances from any part of the equipment which may be a source of ignition (eg by suitable enclosure) or should ensure that the equipment operates at sufficiently low temperature and energy levels as not to be a source of ignition under likely conditions of use and fault.

Classification system of ingress protection (IP rating)

22 There is an internationally recognised system of classifying the degree of protection provided by enclosures against the ingress of solid objects and moisture, and the protection afforded against contact with any live parts within the enclosure for all types of electrical equipment. The system is commonly known as the IP rating system (IP = Index of Protection) and is detailed in a number of standards which are listed in Appendix 2.

Regulation 7

Insulation, protection and placing of conductors

*All **conductors** in a **system** which may give rise to **danger** shall either -*

> *(a) be suitably covered with insulating material and as necessary protected so as to prevent, so far as is reasonably practicable, **danger**; or*
>
> *(b) have such precautions taken in respect of them (including, where appropriate, their being suitably placed) as will prevent, so far as is reasonably practicable, **danger**.*

1   The regulation requires that danger be prevented, so far as is reasonably practicable, by the means detailed in either part (a) or (b).

2   The danger to be protected against generally arises from differences in electrical potential (voltage) between circuit conductors or between such conductors and other conductors in a system - usually conductors at earth potential. The conventional approach is either to insulate the conductors or to

so place them that persons are unable to receive an electric shock or burn from these conductors.

3   Some form of basic insulation, or physical separation, of conductors in a system is necessary for the system to function. That functional minimum, however, may not be sufficient to comply with the requirements of regulation 7. Factors which must be taken into account are:

(a) the nature and severity of the probable danger;

(b) the functions to be performed by the equipment;

(c) the location of the equipment, its environment and the conditions to which it will be subjected;

(d) any work which is likely to be performed upon, with or near the equipment.

Insulation

4   Regulation 7(a) states the requirement that conductors are to be insulated. Suitable insulation of the conductors in an electrical system is, in the majority of cases, the primary and necessary safeguard to prevent danger from electric shock, either between live conductors or between a live conductor and earth. It will also prevent danger from fire and explosion arising from contact of conductors either with each other or with earth. Energy from quite low levels of voltage (and levels insufficient to create a shock risk) can ignite a flammable atmosphere. The quality and effectiveness of insulation therefore needs to be commensurate with the voltages applied to the conductors and the conditions of use.

5   The IEE Wiring Regulations give some advice on these matters for fixed electrical installations up to 1000 volts. See Appendix 2.

6   The Regulation then requires that the insulation be protected as necessary, so that danger may be prevented so far as is reasonably practicable. Mainly, the protection required is in order to prevent mechanical damage to the insulation but may include any of the effects detailed under Regulation 6. Examples of such protection would be the use of steel trunking and conduits or the use of steel armoured cables.

Other precautions including placing

7   Regulation 7(b) permits the alternative of having such precautions taken in respect of the conductors. These precautions may include the suitable placing of the conductors. The precautions may comprise strictly controlled working practices reinforced by measures such as written instructions, training and warning notices etc. The precautions must prevent danger so far as is reasonably practicable. Examples where bare conductors are used in conjunction with suitable precautions are to be found in many applications including overhead electric power lines, down-shop conductors for overhead travelling cranes in factories etc, railway electrification using either separate conductor and running rails or overhead pick-up wires, and certain large electrolytic and electrothermal plants.

8   The design and construction of overhead electric power lines is specified in statutory Regulations which are administered by the Engineering Inspectorate of the Department of Trade and Industry. (See Introduction.)

9   Electric railway and tramway operators, in conjunction with the Railway Inspectorate, have developed standards and safety specifications for the construction of those parts of their systems which use bare conductors at overhead and at track level, together with safe systems of work.

10 Safety is ensured in electrochemical plants which use high current by such means as the separation of conductors which are at different potentials, the use of insulating working platforms and unearthed or isolated electrical supplies. (See paragraphs 14-16.)

11 Suitable placing of the conductors may alone go a considerable way towards preventing danger, for example where the conductors are within a secure enclosure or where they are placed overhead at such a height that contact with these conductors is not reasonably foreseeable. Guidance on the security and protection of enclosures and the measure of their accessibility as determined by standard (finger) tests is given in standards listed in Appendix 2.

12 However, if the placing of the conductors cannot alone be relied upon to prevent danger, then additional precautions need to be taken and rigorously applied. For example, in the case of live railway conductor rails the precautions may include warning notices, barriers and special training for railway staff. Electrolytic and electrothermal processes are further examples and these are the subject of paragraph 14.

13 Duty holders should carefully consider the inherent risks that may exist if bare conductors are merely placed where they cannot normally be touched. Firstly, the protection of the equipment is required under regulation 6 for a range of reasonably foreseeable effects and secondly, there may be occasions when persons will require access to the area or enclosure where such conductors are located, eg substations and test areas. Where work is to be done with the conductors live, regulation 14 is relevant and the guidance under that regulation also applies.

Electrolytic and electrothermal processes

14 It is often necessary, in connection with industrial electrolytic and electrothermal processes, including large secondary battery installations, to adopt a range of precautions. As the work activity is likely to be near the live and uninsulated conductors the precautions adopted will go towards satisfying both part (b) of regulation 7 and regulation 14.

15 Precautions may include:

(a) segregating the process area and limiting access to those people who are trained and experienced in the process and to persons who are supervised so that injuries are prevented;

(b) ensuring a separation of conductors appropriate to the difference in potentials;

(c) use of insulating work platforms;

(d) use of electrical supplies which are isolated from earth together with protective devices to ensure this isolation;

(e) exclusion of unnecessary conducting materials and implements from the process area;

(f) use of protective clothing, eg in electric arc welding processes, protective clothing offers protection against both the hot welding process and against the electric shock risk.

16 Details of advice on the safe use of electric induction furnaces and electric arc welding is given in Appendix 1.

Regulation 8

Earthing or other suitable precautions

Precautions shall be taken, either by earthing or by other suitable means, to prevent **danger** *arising when any* **conductor** *(other than a* **circuit conductor***) which may reasonably foreseeably become charged as a result of either the use of a* **system***, or a fault in a* **system***, becomes so charged; and, for the purposes of ensuring compliance with this regulation, a* **conductor** *shall be regarded as earthed when it is connected to the general mass of earth by* **conductors** *of sufficient strength and current-carrying capability to discharge electrical energy to earth.*

1 The defence (regulation 29) is available in any proceedings for an offence under this regulation.

2 The regulation applies to any conductor, other than a circuit conductor, which is liable to become charged either as a result of the use of a system or a fault in a system. The regulation requires that precautions be taken to prevent danger resulting from that conductor becoming charged.

3 Because the regulation applies to any conductor (other than circuit conductors), this may include the conductive parts of equipment, such as outer metallic casings, which can be touched, which although not live, may become live under fault conditions.

4 Conductors which, although not part of a system, are within electrostatic or electromagnetic fields created by a system may be subject to this regulation. Appropriate precautions are necessary if the induced voltages or currents are large enough to give rise to danger.

Dangers

5 Dangers which may arise as a result of failure to take the necessary precautions include:

(a) risk of shock from such conductors which are or may be exposed so that they may be touched and which become charged at dangerous voltage relative to earth or to other exposed conductors;

(b) risk of burns, fire, arcing or explosion due to currents of excessive magnitude and/or duration in such conductors.

6 The requirements of the regulation may be responded to in several different ways, depending on the circumstances, including:

(a) ensuring that such conductors do not become charged. This has the effect of excluding the conductors from the scope of this regulation;

(b) ensuring that if such conductors do become charged the values of voltage and current and the duration are such that danger will not arise;

(c) ensuring that if such conductors do become charged the environment is such that danger will not arise.

7   Techniques employed for achieving the above include:

(a)   double insulation;

(b)   earthing;

(c)   connection to a common voltage reference point on the system;

(d)   equipotential bonding;

(e)   use of safe voltages;

(f)   earth-free non-conducting environments;

(g)   current/energy limitation; and

(h)   separated or isolated systems.

The above techniques may be employed singly or in combination.

(a) Double insulation

8   The principle of 'double insulation' is that the live conductors of the electrical equipment are covered by two discrete layers or components of insulation each of which would adequately insulate the conductor but which together ensure an improbability of danger arising from insulation failure. This arrangement avoids the need for any external metalwork of the equipment to be connected to a protective conductor or to earth. Double insulation has been found to be particularly suitable for certain types of portable equipment, eg electric motor driven tools etc, and the need for an earthing protective conductor is eliminated. See Appendix 2 for relevant standards. However, the integrity of this protective provision for safety depends upon the layers of insulation remaining in sound condition and this in turn requires that the equipment be properly constructed, used and maintained.

(b) Earthing

9   It is the practice in the UK for the public electricity supply system at the usual distribution pressures of 230 volts single phase, 400 volts three phase, to be referenced to earth by a deliberate electrical connection made at the distribution substations or power transformers. It is the existence of this system earthing which enables earth faults on electrical equipment to be detected and the electrical supply to faulty equipment to be cut off automatically.

10   Many 240/400 volt power installations are so designed that the automatic interruption of the supply upon the occurrence of an earth fault is performed by fuses or automatic circuit breakers (MCBs etc). In most cases these devices will have been selected to provide the additional protective function of interrupting excess current required under regulation 11. In these circumstances it is essential that the earth fault current be large enough to rupture the fuse quickly. The magnitude of the fault current under full earth fault conditions is governed mainly by the combined impedance of the fault loop which will include the impedance of the fault itself, that of the earthing or protective conductors, the circuit conductors and that of the source. Tests should therefore be carried out on new installations and at appropriate intervals thereafter to ascertain that the earth fault (loop) impedances are low enough to ensure that the electrical protective devices such as fuses, circuit

breakers etc will operate in the event of a breakdown of insulation leading to an 'earth fault'.

11   Acceptable parameters of earth loop impedance and interruption times etc for final installations up to 1000 volts may be found in the IEE Wiring Regulations (see Appendix 2). It is rarely sufficient to rely upon an earth rod or rods to provide sufficient conductance for return fault currents. Separate protective earth cables or conductors connected to the neutral point of the supply are usually necessary unless other measures such as the use of sensitive residual current protection equipment is used to detect earth fault currents.

12   For the duration of the fault, the electrical bonding of exposed conductive parts and their connection to earth serves to limit the shock risk from the transient voltages appearing between metallic enclosures of equipment in the system or between a metallic enclosure and earth. Equipment earthing therefore includes the bonding of metallic enclosures, cable armouring, conduits and trunking etc, so that these conductors are electrically continuous and securely connected to the general mass of earth at one or more points.

13   Earthing and bonding conductors must be suitable for the maximum current which they may carry under fault conditions and be capable of surviving the worst case fault (see paragraph 3 of the guidance to regulation 5). Their construction and strength must be adequate to withstand likely wear and tear. Where it might otherwise be difficult to ensure the continued effectiveness of earthing and bonding arrangements it may be necessary to provide supplementary protection such as protective earth conductor monitoring.

14   Many accidents have been caused by the metalwork of portable or transportable equipment becoming live as a result of the combined effects of a fault and high impedance protective conductor connections. The danger may be reduced by the use of a residual current device (RCD) designed to operate rapidly at small leakage currents (typically not exceeding 30 MA) although these devices do not eliminate the risk of electric shock. RCDs should be considered only as providing a second line of defence. They should be operated regularly using the test trip button. This test trip procedure is important in maintaining the effectiveness of most types of RCD.

15   Electric arc welding brings special problems associated with earthing practices. Stray currents from electrical arc welding can damage the protective earthing conductors of electrical installations. Advice on electric arc welding safety is given in an HSE publication listed in Appendix 1.

16   Information on earthing practice is available in a number of publications, some of which are listed in Appendix 2.

(c) Connection to a common voltage reference point on the system

17 In the case of UK public electricity supply systems where transformer neutral points are connected to earth, the voltage reference point is the general mass of earth. Other reference points, to which systems may be referenced and to which bonding conductors are connected, may be chosen to suit particular circumstances.

(d) Equipotential bonding

18   Equipotential bonding is the electrical interconnection of all exposed and extraneous conductors, which may become electrically charged, in such a way that dangerous voltages between any of the conductors which may be simultaneously touched are limited.

8

24

(e) Use of safe voltages

19   Reduced voltage systems are particularly appropriate for portable and transportable equipment, in highly conducting locations such as boilers and tunnels where the risk of mechanical damage to equipment and trailing cables is high, where the body may be damp and have large areas of contact with the conducting location and on construction sites.

20   One example is that of building or construction site supply systems operating at 55-0-55V a.c. single phase, or at ll0V three phase with a phase-earth voltage of 64V a.c. Another example is that of an extra low voltages system operating at or below 50V a.c. or 120V d.c. as recommended internationally. Supply systems like these are referenced to earth and are therefore a special case of systems operating at reduced voltage for which bonding and earthing of all metallic enclosures are still recommended.

21   Further advice on reduced voltage systems may be found in HSE guidance notes listed in Appendix I and the IEE Wiring Regulations (see Appendix 2).

(f) Earth-free, non-conducting environments

22   If a system is supplied from a source which is earth-referenced, the path for fault current and the existence of dangerous potentials to earth can be eliminated in a defined area by ensuring that the area is 'earth-free'. This does not necessarily mean that metallic components or fittings need to be prohibited but rather that no part of the defined area is earthed. It is easier to ensure the integrity of an 'earth-free' area by constructing it from non-metallic components in which case it is more appropriately known as a non-conducting location or area. 'Earth-free' and 'non-conducting' areas are of rather specialised application and are used mainly in certain types of testing of electrical equipment, advice on which is available in the publications on electrical testing listed in Appendices 1 and 2.

(g) Current limitation

23   If fault currents which could cause electric shock are inherently limited by appropriate passive devices, eg high integrity resistors, then protection by earthing or other means may not be required. In the conventional dry, working environment, for example, if the current is limited preferably to one milliampere but certainly to no more than 5 mA (milliamperes) this will not usually present a risk of injury from electric shock to persons in good health who may be subjected to it only occasionally and for a short time only. However, even this low level of current may give perceptible shock which although by itself is unlikely to be physiologically dangerous, may give rise to a consequential injury such as from a fall induced by the shock (but see earlier paragraph on 'injury' under regulation 2, especially IEC publication 479, BS PD 6519 (see Appendix 2)).

(h) Separated or isolated systems

24   If safety depends on the supply system not being referenced to its immediate environment, whether true earth or surrounding metalwork, no potential should normally exist between live conductors and earth or exposed metallic parts. However, all systems are to some extent referenced to their environment by capacitive or inductive coupling or by leakage. For this reason, reliance cannot necessarily be placed on the circuit conductors of separated or isolated* systems being at zero potential relative to their environment. Unless the isolated system is a very small and localised one, the leakage current may

---

* 'Isolated' in this context means separate from all other systems and does not imply 'isolation' as defined specifically for the purpose of regulation 12.

be large enough to provide a path for a fatal electric shock. Any difference in potential is likely to be greatest on extensive systems but, in all cases when the voltages or currents could be dangerous, precautions are needed. Examples of isolated systems are those supplied from the secondary winding of an isolating transformer or the winding of an alternator where there is no connection between them and any other source of electrical energy.

25   The isolation of a power system from earth may reduce the risks associated with a single fault. However, if this first fault has the effect of referencing the system to earth or other exposed conductor, subsequent faults may lead to very destructive and hazardous short circuits so extra precautions will be necessary to prevent this danger. These may include the bonding of metallic enclosures; earth fault detection; insulation monitoring or the use of an earth-free non-conducting environment. Regular inspection and testing to ensure that system isolation integrity is maintained will also be necessary.

Regulation 9

Integrity of referenced conductors

*If a **circuit conductor** is connected to earth or to any other reference point, nothing which might reasonably be expected to give rise to **danger** by breaking the electrical continuity or introducing high impedance shall be placed in that conductor unless suitable precautions are taken to prevent that **danger**.*

1   The defence (regulation 29) is available in any proceedings for an offence under this regulation.

2   In many circumstances the reference point is earthed because the majority of power distribution installations are so referenced by a deliberate connection to earth at the generators or distribution transformers.

3   The object of the regulation is to prevent referenced circuit conductors which should be at or about the same potential as the reference point from reaching significantly different potentials thereby giving rise to possible danger.

4   The most common situation in which this regulation is relevant is in systems having a neutral point which is earthed. Such systems can be sub-divided:

(a)   systems, or parts of systems, in which the neutral and protective conductor are combined (eg TN-C and the combined parts of TN-C-S systems);*

(b)   systems or parts of systems in which the neutral and protective conductors are separate (eg TN-S and the separate parts of TN-C-S systems).

Devices placed in the conductor

5   The regulation does not prohibit all electrical devices from being placed in referenced conductors. For example, a proper joint or a bolted link or a bar primary current transformer can be arranged to ensure the integrity of the conductor.

6   The regulation would also permit the inclusion of other devices such as a removable link, or even a manually-operated knife switch, provided that

*This terminology is explained in Part 2 of the IEE Wiring Regulations, 16th Edition.

suitable precautions are adopted to ensure that these devices are not removed or operated in such a way as to give rise to danger. However, a number of other devices such as fuses, thyristors, transistors etc generally cannot be relied upon not to give rise to danger by becoming open circuit or introducing high impedance into the conductor. The regulation prohibits such applications.

Combined neutral and protective conductors

7   Open circuit of, or high impedance in, combined neutral and protective conductors will almost certainly result in the exposed and extraneous conductors which are connected to the protective conductors, eg metal enclosures of switchgear, being at a significant potential (up to phase-neutral volts) relative to earth. This could lead to a risk of electric shock or burn, thus the integrity of the combined neutral and earth conductor is very important. However, where the protective conductor is combined with the neutral conductor over some part of their length, precautions to prevent persons coming into simultaneous contact with the protective conductors and earth (or conductors at earth potential) should be taken. Equipotential bonding of all metalwork within a building and the connection of this to the protective conductor or neutral is a commonly used approach. Generally, however, CNE systems should be confined to the public electricity supply network up to the point of supply to consumers.

Separate neutral and protective conductors

8   When deciding whether danger may result where there are separate neutral and protective conductors it is necessary to consider not only the normal operation of the system but also the situations that may arise when work is being carried out on or near the system. If voltage rises on the neutral conductor could result in danger during the work then the above restrictions on devices in the neutral should be observed. For example, a fuse should not be placed in a neutral of a fixed power distribution installation (typically 230 volts) because this places persons working on the installation at risk of electric shock and burn should that fuse operate or otherwise become open circuit. Double pole fusing (fuses in both the phase and neutral) is acceptable, however, if these are fitted within self-contained electrical equipment which itself is not part of the fixed electrical installation and is connected to the fixed installation by a plug and socket by means of which the equipment may be readily isolated from the system prior to work being done on that equipment.

9   In general, if a neutral conductor is to be switched, a multipole switch or circuit breaker should be used which also switches all of the related phase conductors, the neutral breaking last and making first. Such switching should not interrupt the protective conductor.

Regulation 10   Connections

*Where necessary to prevent **danger**, every joint and connection in a **system** shall be mechanically and electrically suitable for use.*

1   The defence (regulation 29) is available in any proceedings for an offence under this regulation.

Suitability of connections

2   The regulation requires that all connections in circuit and protective

27

conductors, including connections to terminals, plugs and sockets, and any other means of joining or connecting conductors, should be suitable for the purposes for which they are used. This requirement applies equally to temporary and permanent connections.

3   The insulation and conductance of the connections should be suitable, having regard to the conditions of use including likely fault conditions.

4   The mechanical protection and strength should be such as to ensure the integrity of the insulation and conductance under all conditions of use including likely fault conditions, subject to the need for any maintenance which may be required by regulation 4(2).

5   Joints and connections in protective conductors should be made at least as carefully as those in circuit conductors and they should be of sufficient strength and conductance to allow for the passage of fault currents. Such connections may need to be treated so as to prevent corrosion. It is recommended that combinations of metals liable to produce damaging electrolytic action be avoided.

Plugs and sockets

6   Plug and socket connections and their use should be so arranged that accidental contact with conductors live at dangerous voltages is prevented. Mainly this should be achieved by selection of appropriate equipment but may involve some degree of operator skill and/or training depending on the circumstances.

7   In most applications, where a plug and socket type connector conveys a protective conductor as well as the circuit conductors, the protective conductor should be the first to be made and the last to be separated. The use of equipment made to appropriate standards should ensure that the principle is adhered to.

8   Where plug and socket connections are not rated for making or breaking the maximum load current, effective arrangements should be made, for example, by mechanical interlocking with the switch that controls the power, to ensure that the connections are made or broken only under no-load conditions.

Portable equipment

9   Special attention should be given to joints and connections in cables and equipment which will be handled, for example flexible cables for portable equipment. Plugs and sockets for portable equipment should be constructed in accordance with appropriate Standards and arranged that, where necessary, earthing of any metal casing of the equipment is automatically effected by the insertion of the plug. HSE guidance notes and British Standards give further guidance on portable equipment (see Appendices 1 and 2).

Means for protecting from excess of current

*Efficient means, suitably located, shall be provided for protecting from excess of current every part of a **system** as may be necessary to prevent **danger**.*

1   The defence (regulation 29) is available in any proceedings for an offence under this regulation. (See commentary, paragraphs 11 to 13).

2   It is recognised that faults and overloads may occur on electrical systems.

The regulation requires that systems and parts of systems be protected against the effects of short circuits and overloads if these would result in currents which would otherwise result in danger.

3   The means of protection is likely to be in the form of fuses or circuit breakers controlled by relays etc or it may be provided by some other means capable of interrupting the current or reducing it to a safe value.

The need to anticipate abnormal conditions

4   The regulation requires the means of preventing danger to be provided in anticipation of excess current; a fault or overload need not have occurred. Fault currents arise as a result of short circuits between conductors caused either by inherent failure of the electrical equipment or some outside influence, eg mechanical damage to a cable. Overload currents can arise as a result of the inadequacy of a system to supply the load and may be caused by an increased demand created by outside influence on the electrical equipment, eg mechanical overloading of an electric motor.

The selection of excess current protection

5   In principle, every main circuit should be protected at its origin, ie at the source end of the circuit. Where the rating of the conductors forming a branch circuit is less than that of the conductors from which it is drawing power, it is conventional for protection to be placed at this point. In practice, however, there are exceptions to this principle and, depending on the nature of the system, a technical judgement must be made as to where the protection should be placed. Guidance on some aspects of this subject is given in the IEE Wiring Regulations (see Appendix 2).

6   When selecting the means of protection, consideration must be given to a number of factors among the more important of which are:

(a)   the nature of the circuits and type of equipment to be protected;

(b)   the short circuit energy available in the supply (the fault level);

(c)   the nature of the environment;

(d)   whether the system is earthed or not.

(a) The nature of the circuits and type of equipment to be protected

7   The circuits to be dealt with may vary from high power high voltage circuits, for example for the inter-connection of substations or for the supply to large motors, down to the smallest final circuit supplying a few low power lamps at say 6 volts. Over this range lies a great diversity of equipment each item of which will possess characteristics which must be carefully considered in the selection of appropriate devices to protect against excess current.

(b) Fault level

8   Due regard must be paid to the maximum short circuit current with which the protective device may have to deal. (The ability of circuit breakers and fuses to operate successfully and without dangerous effects, serious arcing or, in the case of oil-filled equipment, the liberation of oil, is implicit in the requirements of regulations 4 and 5.) The design of the protective arrangement must also provide for sufficient current to be available to operate the protective devices correctly in respect of all likely faults.

(c) The nature of the environment

9   The nature of the environment may have a bearing on the choice of protective devices and their settings, for example where the possibility of a fire being started may be considerable. In all cases, however, the protection against excess current must be effective so that short circuits and earth faults are cleared promptly to minimise destructive arcing and heating. Protective devices whether they be circuit breakers or fuses should therefore be set or selected for the minimum tripping currents and times consistent with ensuring the reliable operation of the device and for the need for discrimination between successive stages of protection.

(d) Earthed system

10   Where a system is earthed the nature and efficiency of the earthing system is important in relation to the design and reliability of the protective devices. In earthed systems, ie where some part of the windings of the machine or transformer from which the supply is derived is connected to earth, operation in the event of an earth fault of the protective device, whether circuit breaker or fuse, is dependent on sufficient current passing to operate the excess current or earth leakage tripping device or to blow the fuse. In many systems, the device provided in pursuance of the requirements of this regulation in respect of excess of current (very often a fuse) may also provide protection against earth faults - and thus be in pursuance of the requirements of regulation 8.

Defence in criminal proceedings

11   The defence (regulation 29) is available in any proceedings for an offence under this regulation.

12   In some circumstances it will be technically impossible to achieve total compliance with the absolute requirement to prevent danger. If an excess of current is drawn due to a fault or overload, for example due to an arcing fault, then whatever form of electrical protection is provided, there will be some danger at the point of the fault during the finite time taken for the detection and interruption of the fault current. Nevertheless, the choice of electrical protection, be it by means of a simple fuse or whatever, must be properly chosen and installed in accordance with good electrical engineering practice. The protection must be efficient and effective.

13   In some circumstances it is undesirable to interrupt the current in a circuit because this may itself lead to a hazard. Examples of such circumstances include the excitation field current of direct current motors, trip coil circuits, lifting electromagnets and the secondary circuits of current transformers. In such cases, however, the circuit should be so rated or arranged not to give rise to danger from excess of current.

11

Regulation 12

Means for cutting off the supply and for isolation

*(1)   Subject to paragraph (3), where necessary to prevent **danger**, suitable means (including, where appropriate, methods of identifying circuits) shall be available for -*

*(a)   cutting off the supply of electrical energy to any **electrical equipment**; and*

12

*(b)   the isolation of any **electrical equipment**.*

*(2)   In paragraph (1), "isolation" means the disconnection and separation of the **electrical equipment** from every source of electrical energy in such a way that this disconnection and separation is secure.*

*(3)   Paragraph (1) shall not apply to **electrical equipment** which is itself a source of electrical energy but, in such a case as is necessary, precautions shall be taken to prevent, so for as is reasonably practicable, **danger**.*

1   The defence (regulation 29) is available in any proceedings for an offence under this regulation.

Regulation 12(1)(a)

2   The objective of this part of the regulation is to ensure that, where necessary to prevent danger, suitable means are available by which the electricity supply to any piece of equipment can be switched off. Switching can be, for example, by direct manual operation or by indirect operation via 'stop' buttons in the control circuits of contactors or circuit breakers. There may be a need to switch off electrical equipment for reasons other than preventing electrical danger but these considerations are outside the scope of the Regulations.

Regulation 12(1)(b)

3   Whereas regulation 12(1)(a) requires means to be provided whereby the supply of electrical energy can be switched off, 12(1)(b) requires that there will be available suitable means of ensuring that the supply will remain switched off and inadvertent reconnection prevented. This is isolation. This provision, in conjunction with safe working practices, will enable work to be carried out on electrical equipment without risk of it becoming live during the course of that work, for example if the work is to be done under the terms of regulation 13.

4   In some cases the equipment used to perform the requirement under regulation 12(1)(a) may also serve to perform the requirement under 12(1)(b). It must be understood that the two functions of *switching* off and *isolation* are not the same, even though in some circumstances they are performed by the same action or by the same equipment.

Regulation 12(3)

5   Regulation 12(3) recognises the impracticability in some cases of switching off or of isolating that equipment which is itself an integral part of a source of electrical energy, for example the terminals of accumulators, large capacitors and the windings of generators. The regulation requires precautions to be taken in these circumstances so that danger is prevented so far as is reasonably practicable. See Appendix 1 for guidance on working practices.

"Where necessary to prevent danger"

6   The need for means to cut off the supply and effect isolation depends on factors such as likely danger in normal and abnormal conditions. This assessment may be influenced by environmental conditions and provisions to be made in case of emergencies, such as a fire in a premises. It includes consideration of which electrical equipment could be a source of danger if such means were not provided and of the installation, commissioning, operational and maintenance requirements over the life of the equipment.

Suitable means for cutting off the supply

7   The suitable means for cutting off the supply (regulation 12(1)(a)) should:

(a)   be capable of cutting off the supply under all likely conditions having regard to the equipment, its normal operation conditions, any abnormal operating or fault conditions, and the characteristics of the source(s) of electrical energy;

(b)   be in a suitable location having regard to the nature of the risks, the availability of persons to operate the means and the speed at which operation may be necessary. Access to switches etc should be kept clear and unobstructed, free of tripping and slipping hazards etc;

(c)   be clearly marked so as to show its relationship to the equipment which it controls, unless there could be no doubt that this would be obvious to any person who may need to operate it; and

(d)   only be common to several items of electric equipment where it is appropriate for these to be energised and de-energised as a group.

Suitable means of isolation

8   The suitable means of isolation of equipment (regulation 12(1)(b)) should:

(a)   have the capability to positively establish an air gap or other effective dielectric, which together with adequate creepage and clearance distances, will ensure that there is no likely way in which the isolation gap can fail electrically;

(b)   include, where necessary, means directed at preventing unauthorised interference with or improper operation of the equipment, for example means of locking off;

(c)   be located so that the accessibility and ease with which it may be employed is appropriate for the application. The time and effort which must be expended in order to effect isolation should be reasonable having regard to the nature of the equipment and the circumstances under which isolation may be required, eg a very remote means of isolation may be acceptable if isolation is only needed infrequently and any additional time taken to effect isolation does not result in danger;

(d)   be clearly marked so as to show to which equipment it relates, unless there could be no doubt that this would be obvious to any person who may need to operate it;

(e)   only be common to several items of electrical equipment where it is appropriate for these to be isolated as a group.

Selection of isolator switches

9   Isolator switches (or disconnecters) will often be employed as the means of effecting disconnection and secure separation from the supply. In selecting appropriate equipment to perform this function particular regard should be given to:

(a)   the isolating distances between contacts or other means of isolation which should be in accordance with an appropriate Standard or be otherwise equally effective;

(b)   the position of the contacts or other means of isolation which should either be externally visible or clearly and reliably indicated. An indication of the isolated position, other than by direct observation of the isolating gap, should occur when the specified isolating distance has been achieved in each pole;

(c)   provision to enable the prevention of unauthorised, improper or unintentional energisation, eg locking off facilities.

10   For further information on the selection of isolators/disconnectors reference should be made to appropriate standards, see Appendix 2.

Regulation 13   Precautions for work on equipment made dead

*Adequate precautions shall be taken to prevent **electrical equipment**, which has been mode dead in order to prevent **danger** while work is carried out on or near that equipment, from becoming electrically charged during that work if **danger** may thereby arise.*

1   The defence (regulation 29) is available in any proceedings for an offence under this regulation.

2   Regulation 13 relates to situations in which electrical equipment has been made dead in order that work either on it or near it may be carried out without danger. The regulation may apply during any work, be it electrical or non-electrical. The regulation requires adequate precautions to be taken to prevent the electrical equipment from becoming electrically charged, from whatever source, if this charging would give rise to danger. 'Charged' is discussed under regulation 2.

3   The regulation uses the term 'electrical equipment' which is defined by regulation 2. This will include any cables, conductors, wires, connectors etc which may have been arranged to connect together the various other items of electrical plant or equipment such as motors, transformers, switch gear etc. The regulation may therefore apply to any or all of these.

The precautions

4   The precautions should be effective in preventing the electrical equipment from becoming charged in any way which would give rise to danger.

5   In the first place the procedures for making the equipment dead will probably involve use of the means required by regulation 12(1)(a) for cutting off the supply of electrical energy. Isolation of the electrical equipment will be necessary and the means required by regulation 12(1)(b) will facilitate this. Ideally a means of locking off an isolator can be used. Where such facilities are not available, the removal of fuses or links and their being held in safe keeping can provide a secure arrangement if proper control procedures are used.

6   These precautions will prevent the equipment from becoming charged by connection to its own or normal sources of electrical energy but may not alone

33

be sufficient to prevent charging. The presence of electrical energy as a result of electromagnetic induction, mutual capacitance or stored electrical energy may have to be guarded against, for example by applying earthing connections for the duration of the work (temporary earths). The precautions may need to include means of preventing further accumulation of electrical charge, following initial discharge, because latent energy may be stored in the system, for example in the dielectric of high voltage cables. In the case of work upon high voltage power distribution circuits isolation procedures should include the back-up measure of applying circuit main earths (primary earths) at points of isolation by means of purpose-built facilities.

7   Where work is to be done on or near conductors that have been isolated, the conductors should be proved dead at the point of work before the work starts. Where a test instrument or voltage indicator is used for this purpose this should itself be proved, preferably immediately before and immediately after testing the conductor. (See also regulation 4(3).)

8   The regulation does not preclude the application of a test voltage to equipment provided that this does not give rise to danger.

Written procedures

9   It may also be appropriate for the safety isolation procedures to be formalised in written instructions or house rules. 'Permits-to-work' may form part of the written procedures and their use is considered essential to ensuring a safe system of work where this involves work on the conductors or equipment of high voltage power distribution systems (typically where the working voltage exceeds 3000 volts) or where the system is very complex. Properly formulated and regulated 'permit-to work' procedures focus the minds both of those issuing and of those receiving the permits both on the manner in which the work is to be done and on how the equipment has been made safe. Further advice on these procedures and precautions may be found in the guidance listed in Appendices 1 and 2.

Decommissioned equipment

10   Before electrical equipment is decommissioned, dismantled or abandoned for any reason it should be disconnected from all sources of supply and effective steps taken to ensure that it is dead and cannot inadvertently become re-energised or dangerously charged. It may be necessary to securely mark or otherwise suitably label equipment, circuits, switches etc to guard against inadvertent re-energisation. (See also the requirement for identifying circuits under regulation 12(1).)

Regulation 14

Work on or near live conductors

*No person shall be engaged in any work activity on or so near any live **conductor** (other than one suitably covered with insulating material so as to prevent **danger**) that **danger** may arise unless -*

(a)   *it is unreasonable in all the circumstances for it to be dead; and*

(b)   *it is reasonable in **all** the circumstances for him to be at work on or near it while it is live; and*

(c)   *suitable precautions (including where necessary the provision of suitable protective equipment) are taken to prevent **injury**.*

14

34

1   The defence (regulation 29) is available in any proceedings for an offence under this regulation.

2   Regulation 14 addresses the situation where, either permanently or temporarily, danger from conductors is not prevented by the precautions specified in regulation 7(a).

3   The regulation is concerned only with those situations where persons are at work on or near live electrical conductors which may foreseeably give rise to danger. Such work is permitted only if conditions (a) and (b) and (c) are satisfied. 'Work' is not confined to electrical work but includes any work activity.

(a) The need for the conductor to be live

4   If danger may otherwise arise it is always preferable from the point of view of safety that work on or near such electrical equipment should be carried out when that equipment is dead. (See regulation 13 and guidance.) Regulation 14 recognises that there are circumstances, however, in which it is unreasonable, having regard to all relevant factors, for the equipment to be dead while work proceeds. An example of this might be where it was found necessary to undertake some maintenance, checking or repair on a busy section of electric railway track where it would be disproportionately disruptive and costly in many ways for the live conductors to be isolated for the period of the work. Other examples are to be found in the electrical supply industry, particularly live cable jointing, and in much of the work done on telephone network connections.

5   Equipment users should bear in mind at the time of ordering, purchase and installation of plant, the manner of operation, maintenance and repair of the electrical equipment which will be necessary during the life of the plant.

6   It is recommended that the design of electrical equipment and of the installation should eliminate the need for live work which puts persons at risk of injury. This can often be done by careful thought at the design stage of installations, for example by the provision of alternative power infeeds, properly laid out distribution systems to allow parts to be isolated for work to proceed and by designing equipment housings etc to give segregation of parts to be worked on and protect persons from other parts which may be live.

7   It is recommended that equipment which combines power and control circuitry should be arranged so that the power circuits are physically separate and segregated from logic and control circuits or so placed, recessed or otherwise arranged that the risk of accidental contact is eliminated. Diagnostic work on the low power/voltage circuits may then proceed with less risk to personnel. Where regular measurements of say voltage, current etc are to be made, consideration should be given to appropriate test and measuring equipment, eg voltmeters, ammeters, etc or test points being built into the equipment.

8   Live work includes live testing, for example the use of a potential indicator on mains power and control logic circuits (but see paragraph 20).

9   The factors which would be considered in deciding whether it was justifiable for work to proceed with the conductors live would include the following:

(a)   when it is not practicable to carry out the work with the conductors dead, eg where for the purposes of testing it is necessary for the conductors to be live;

(b) the creation of other hazards, by making the conductors dead, such as to other users of the system, or for continuously operating process plants etc;

(c) the need to comply with other statutory requirements;

(d) the level of risk involved in working live and the effectiveness of the precautions available set against economic need to perform that work.

(b) The need to be near uninsulated live conductors

10 Persons at work are permitted to be near live conductors only if this is reasonable in all the circumstances. If, for example, it would be reasonable for the work to be carried out at a safe distance from the conductors then it would be prohibited for that work to be done near the conductors.

11 Persons whose presence near the live conductors is not necessary should not be so near the conductors that they are at risk of injury.

(c) The need to take precautions to prevent injury

12 The precautions necessary to comply with regulation 14(c) need to be commensurate with the risk.

13 The system of work should: allow only persons who are competent to do so to work on or near exposed, live conductors (competence for these and other purposes is further dealt with at regulation 16); indicate within what limits the work is to be attempted; indicate what levels of competence apply to each category of such work; and incorporate procedures under which the person attempting the work will report back if the limits specified in the system are likely to be exceeded. This usually requires detailed planning before the work is started.

14 Suitable precautions should include as appropriate:

(a) the use of people who are properly trained and competent to work on live equipment safely (see also regulation 16);

(b) the provision of adequate information to the person carrying out the work about the live conductors involved, the associated electrical system and the foreseeable risks;

(c) the use of suitable tools, including insulated tools, equipment and protective clothing (see also regulation 4(4));

(d) the use of suitable insulated barriers or screens (see also regulation 4(4));

(e) the use of suitable instruments and test probes;

(f) accompaniment by another person or persons if the presence of such person or persons could contribute significantly to ensuring that injury is prevented;

(g) the restriction of routine live test work (for example product testing) to specific areas and the use of special precautions within those areas such as isolated power supplies, non-conducting locations etc;

(h) effective control of any area where there is danger from live conductors.

Accompaniment

15   A duty holder's judgement as to whether a person carrying out work subject to regulation 14 should be accompanied should be based on considerations of how injury is to be prevented. If an accompanying person can substantially contribute towards the implementation of safe working practice, then he should be present. He should be trained to recognise danger and, if necessary, to render assistance in the event of an emergency.

16   Some examples of electrical work where it is likely that the person carrying out the work should be accompanied are:

(a)   electrical work involving manipulation of live, uninsulated, power conductors at say, 230 volts using insulated tools; and

(b)   other work on or near bare live conductors where a person working on their own would not be capable of undertaking the work safely without assistance in, for example, keeping other persons from the work area.

Control of the area

17   Effective control of an area where there is danger from live conductors means ensuring that those who are not competent to prevent the occurrence of injury and those whose presence is unnecessary are not permitted into the area. If the person undertaking the work is continuously present while danger exists from the live conductors, and the area is small enough to be under his constant supervision and control, then further precautions to control access may not be necessary. If, however, the area is too large for the person to exercise effective surveillance, or he is not continuously present, then effective control will need to be secured by other means such as the provision of lockable enclosures or barriers, and warning notices indicating the presence of live conductors.

(The above examples are given without prejudice to the requirements of regulation 14, the criteria of which must be followed in each case before live work is undertaken.)

Testing

18   Regulation 14 will often apply to electrical testing. Testing to establish whether electrical conductors are live or dead should always be done on the assumption that they may be live and therefore it should be assumed that this regulation is applicable until such time as the conductors have been proved dead.

19   When testing for confirmation of a 'dead' circuit, the test instrument or voltage indicator used for this purpose should itself be proved, preferably immediately before and immediately after testing the conductors.

20   Although live testing may be justifiable it does not follow that there will necessarily be justification for subsequent repair work to be carried out live.

Protective equipment

21   Examples of protection of a person from the effects of electricity are suitable clothing including insulating helmets, goggles and gloves, insulating materials used as fixed or temporary screening to prevent electric shock and to prevent short circuit between live conductors or between live conductors and earth, insulating mats and stands to prevent electric shock current via the feet and insulated tools and insulated test probes.

14

22   There should be procedures for the periodic examination and where necessary testing of this protective equipment and replacement as necessary. See also the requirements of regulation 4(4). See Appendices 1 and 2 for further guidance on working procedures, standards etc.

Emergency resuscitation and first aid

23   It may be helpful to place notices or placards giving details of emergency resuscitation procedures in the event of electric shock at those locations where persons may be at greater risk of electric shock than most. Such places might include electrical test areas, sub-stations and laboratories but for resuscitation techniques to be effective, those required to exercise them must receive proper training and regular practice. The Health and Safety (First Aid) Regulations 1981 make various requirements for the provision of suitably trained first aiders at places of work.

Work near underground cables and overhead power lines

24   Serious injuries have occurred during excavation and other work near underground power cables and work under or near overhead power lines. This work comes within the scope of regulation 14 if there is a risk of injury from these cables or power lines.

25   Underground power cables present a risk of serious or fatal injury during excavation or similar work, particularly to persons using hand tools (eg picks, concrete breakers, etc). Precautions should include:

(a)   mapping, recording and marking on site of cable runs;

(b)   use of cable locating devices; and

(c)   safe digging practices.

26   Overhead power lines may be readily accessible to persons working on elevated platforms, scaffolding or roofs. Persons working with tall vehicles such as cranes, tipper lorries, or farm machinery or handling metal ladders, pipes or other long articles may also be at risk from a flashover or contact with overhead power lines.

27   Well established advice on matters in paragraphs 25 and 26 is given in HSE Guidance Notes which are listed in Appendix 1.

Working space, access and lighting

*For the purposes of enabling **injury** to be prevented, adequate working space, adequate means of access, and adequate lighting shall be provided at all **electrical equipment** on which or near which work is being done in circumstances which may give rise to **danger**.*

1   The defence (regulation 29) is available in any proceedings for an offence under this regulation.

2   The purpose of the regulation is to ensure that sufficient space, access and adequate illumination are provided while persons are working on, at or near electrical equipment in order that they may work safely. The requirement is not restricted to those circumstances where live conductors are exposed but applies where any work is being done in circumstances which may give rise to

danger. The regulation makes no requirement for such space, access or illumination to be provided at times other than when work is being done. (But see guidance under regulation 12(1)(a), paragraph 7(b) in respect of safe access to means of cutting off the supply.)

Working space

3   Where there are dangerous exposed live conductors within reach the working space dimensions should be adequate:

(a)   to allow persons to pull back away from the conductors without hazard; and

(b)   if persons need to pass one another, to do so with ease and without hazard.

4   Among the legal provisions revoked upon the coming into force of these Regulations were the Electricity (Factories Act) Special Regulations 1908 and 1944. Regulation 17 of those Regulations specified minimum width and height dimensions of switchboard passageways where there were bare conductors exposed or arranged to be exposed when live so that they may be touched. That regulation and the relevant definitions used are reproduced at Appendix 3 to this Memorandum. The dimensions specified were arrived at after much consideration of the circumstances in a Public Inquiry at the time that those Regulations were being drafted. However, those dimensions can still be taken as providing guidance for an appropriate level of safety in many circumstances and where the voltages do not significantly exceed 3000 volts. This is not to condone the use of equipment having normally bare and exposed conductors if a safe alternative can reasonably be adopted.

Lighting

5   Natural light is preferable to artificial light but where artificial light is necessary it is preferable that this be from a permanent and properly designed installation, for example in indoor switchrooms etc. However, there will always be exceptions and special circumstances where these principles cannot be achieved where handlamps or torches etc will be the sole or most important means of lighting. Whatever level of lighting is used it must be adequate to enable injury to be prevented. See Appendix 1 for further guidance on lighting.

15

Regulation 16

Persons to be competent to prevent danger and injury

*No person shall be engaged in any work activity where technical knowledge or experience is necessary to prevent **danger** or, where appropriate, **injury,** unless he possesses such knowledge or experience, or is under such degree of supervision as may be appropriate having regard to the nature of the work.*

1   The defence (regulation 29) is available in any proceedings for an offence under this regulation.

2   The object of the regulation is to ensure that persons are not placed at risk due to a lack of skills on the part of themselves or others in dealing with electrical equipment.

"... prevent danger or, where appropriate, injury ..."

16

3   This regulation uses both of the terms, 'injury' and 'danger'. The regulation therefore applies to the whole range of work associated with electrical equipment where danger may arise and whether or not danger (or the risk of injury) is actually present during the work. It will include situations where the elimination of the risk of injury, ie the prevention of danger, for the duration of the work is under the control of a person who must therefore possess sufficient technical knowledge or experience, or be so supervised, etc to be capable of ensuring that danger is prevented. For example, where a person is to effect the isolation of some electrical equipment before this person undertakes some work on the equipment, they will require sufficient technical knowledge or experience to prevent danger during the isolation. There will be no danger from the equipment during the work provided that the isolation has been carried out properly; danger will have been prevented but the person doing the work must have sufficient technical knowledge or experience so as to prevent danger during that work, for example by knowing not to work on adjacent 'live' circuits.

4   But the regulation also covers those circumstances where danger is present, ie where there is a risk of injury, as for example where work is being done on live or charged equipment using special techniques and under the terms of regulation 14. In these circumstances persons must possess sufficient technical knowledge or experience or be so supervised etc, to be capable of ensuring that injury is prevented.

Technical knowledge or experience

5   The scope of 'technical knowledge or experience' may include:

(a)   adequate knowledge of electricity;

(b)   adequate experience of electrical work;

(c)   adequate understanding of the system to be worked on and practical experience of that class of system;

(d)   understanding of the hazards which may arise during the work and the precautions which need to be taken;

(e)   ability to recognise at all times whether it is safe for work to continue.

Allocation of responsibilities

6   Employees should be trained and instructed to ensure that they understand the safety procedures which are relevant to their work and should work in accordance with any instructions or rules directed at ensuring safety which have been laid down by their employer.

Supervision

7   The regulation recognises that in many circumstances persons will require to be supervised to some degree where their technical knowledge or experience is not of itself sufficient to ensure that they can otherwise undertake the work safely. The responsibilities of those undertaking the supervision should be clearly stated to them by those duty holders who allocate the responsibilities for supervision and consideration should be given to stating these responsibilities in writing. Where the risks involved are low, verbal instructions are likely to be adequate but as the risk or complexity increase there comes a point where the need for written procedures becomes important in order that instructions may be understood and supervised more rigorously.

Guidance

16

In this context, supervision does not necessarily require continual attendance at the work site, but the degree of supervision and the manner in which it is exercised is for the duty holders to arrange to ensure that danger, or as the case may be, injury, is prevented.

Further advice on working procedures is given in guidance publications listed in Appendix 1.

NOTE Regulations 17 to 28 inclusive apply only to mines (see Statutory Instrument 1989 No 635).

Regulation 29

Defence

Regulation

29

In any proceedings for an offence consisting of a contravention of regulations 4(4), 5, 8, 9, 10, 11, 12, 13, 14, 15, 16 or 25, it shall be a defence for any person to prove that he took all reasonable steps and exercised all due diligence to avoid the commission of that offence.

Guidance

29

Regulation 29 applies only in criminal proceedings. It provides a defence for a duty holder who can establish that he took all reasonable steps and exercised all due diligence to avoid committing an offence under regulations 4(4), 5, 8, 9, 10, 11, 12, 13, 14, 15 or 16. (Regulation 25 applies only to mines.)

Regulation 30

Exemption certificates

Regulation

30

(1)   Subject to paragraph (2), the Health and Safety Executive may, by a certificate in writing, exempt -

(a)   any person;

(b)   any premises;

(c)   any electrical equipment;

(d)   any electrical system;

(e)   any electrical process;

(f)   any activity,

or any class of the above, from any requirement or prohibition imposed by these Regulations and any such exemption may be granted subject to conditions and to a limit of time and may be revoked by a certificate in writing at any time.

(2)   The Executive shall not grant any such exemption unless, having regard to the circumstances of the case, and in particular to -

(a)   the conditions, if any, which it proposes to attach to the exemption; and

(b)   any other requirements imposed by or under any enactment which apply to the case,

it is satisfied that the health and safety of persons who are likely to be affected by the exemption will not be prejudiced in consequence of it.

HSE is given power to issue general or special exemptions and to impose conditions and time limits on them. It is a standard power given to allow the variation of legal duties where, in circumstances unforeseen by those drafting the legislation, they are in practice unnecessary or inappropriate. Exemptions would be granted only in very exceptional circumstances.

Regulation 31

Extension outside Great Britain

These Regulations shall apply to and in relation to premises and activities outside Great Britain to which sections 1 to 59 and 80 to 82 of the Health and Safety at Work etc Act 1974 apply by virtue of Articles 6 and 7 of the Health and Safety at Work etc Act 1974 (Application outside Great Britain) Order 1977[(a)] as they apply within Great Britain.

(a)   SI 197711232.

1   The application of the Regulations is co-extensive with the application of the HSW Act outside Great Britain but within territorial waters as regards the premises and activities (but no others) set out in Articles 6 and 7 of the 1977 Order. Great Britain is the United Kingdom of England and Scotland (Union with Scotland Act 1706).

2   Article 6 of the 1977 Order refers to mines, which are not dealt with in this Memorandum.

3   Article 7 of the 1977 Order refers to construction work, loading and unloading ships, diving and ship repair (see the Order itself for the precise definition).

4   Articles 4 and 5 of the 1977 Order refer to oil rigs and pipelines which thereby are not subject to the Regulations, nor are other premises or activities, outside Great Britain but not referred to in the Order, subject to the Regulations.

5   Equipment manufactured onshore for subsequent use where the Regulations do not apply does not become 'equipment' for the purposes of the Regulations if it will not be used or installed for use in Great Britain. However, if it is energised by connection to a source, eg during testing at a manufacturer's works, it will be subject to the Regulations during such testing.

Regulation 32

Disapplication of duties

The duties imposed by these Regulations shall not extend to -

(a)   the master or crew of a sea-going ship or to the employer of such persons, in relation to the normal ship-board activities of a ships crew under the direction of the master; or

(b)   any person, in relation to any aircraft or hovercraft which is moving under its own power.

Sea-going ships

1   Sea-going ships are subject to other electrical safety legislation which gives protection to persons on board. Regulation 32 disapplies the Electricity at Work Regulations from these ships as far as the normal ship-board activities of a ship's crew under the direction of the master is concerned. It does not disapply them in respect of other work activities however, for example where a shore-based electrical contractor goes on board to carry out electrical work on the ship. That person's activities will be subject to the Regulations within the general applicability of the Regulations and in particular only within the territorial waters as provided for under regulation 31.

Aircraft and hovercraft

2   The Regulations may apply only while an aircraft or hovercraft is not moving under its own power.

Vehicles

3   The Regulations may apply to electrical equipment on vehicles if this equipment may give rise to danger.

Revocations and modifications

(1)   The instruments specified in column 1 of Part I of Schedule 2 are revoked to the extent specified in the corresponding entry in column 3 of that Part.

(2)   The enactments and instruments specified in Part II of Schedule 2 shall be modified to the extent specified in that Part.

(3)   In the Mines and Quarries Act 1954, the Mines and Quarries (Tips) Act 1969[(a)] and the Mines Management Act 1971[(b)], and in regulations mode under any of those Acts, or in health and safety regulations, any reference to any of those Acts shall be treated as including a reference to these Regulations.

(a)   1969 c.10.
(b)   1971 c.20.

1   The Regulations replace or modify a number of statutory provisions in accordance with the intention of the HSW Act section 1(2).

2   Systems and equipment which were subject to provisions which have been revoked are now subject to these Regulations.

Appendix 1

HSE and HSC publications on electrical safety

Guidance Note	Title	Regulations particularly relevant
PM 29	*Electrical hazards from steam/water pressure cleaners* ISBN 0 7176 0813 1	4,6,7,8 and 10
PM 38	*Selection and use of electric handlamps* ISBN 0 11 886360 6	4,6,7,8,10 and 12
GS 6	*Avoidance of danger from overhead electric lines* ISBN 0 7176 1348 8	4,14,15 and 16
GS 38	*Electrical test equipment for use by electricians* ISBN 0 7176 0845 X	10, 14 and 16
GS 50	*Electrical safety at places of entertainment* ISBN 0 7176 1387 9	4,5,6,7,8, 10,11 and 12
HSG38	*Lighting at work* ISBN 0 7176 1232 5	4,13,14 and 15
HSG41	*Petrol filling stations: construction and operation* ISBN 0 7176 0461 6	4,5,6,7,8, 10,11 and 12
HSG47	*Avoiding danger from underground services* ISBN 0 7176 1744 0	4,14 and 16
HSG85	*Electricity at work - safe working practices* ISBN 0 7176 0442 X	4,7,12,13, 14,15 and 16
	Safe use of electric induction furnaces. Health and Safety Commission, Foundries Industry Advisory Committee publication ISBN 0 11 883909 8	4,5,6,7,8,14 15 and 16
HSG118	*Electrical safety in arc welding* ISBN 0 7176 0704 6	4,6,7,8,10,12, 14,16
HSG141	*Electrical safety on construction sites* ISBN 0 7176 1000 4	4-16 inclusive

Note: The publications listed in Appendix 1 are available from HSE Books (see inside back cover for address etc).

Other publications having an electrical safety content

Standards, Codes of Practice and other publications which contain guidance relevant to the Regulations and electrical safety, which have been published by bodies other than either HSE or HSC, are given in this appendix. Most of these documents are the product of technical committees on which HSE has been represented. This does not mean, however, that the documents are concerned solely with safety and users should bear in mind the scope of the safety content of these documents and the fact that they have largely been arrived at through a process of consensus.

Note: British Standards Institution publications are obtainable from BSI Sales and Customer Services, 389 Chiswick High Road, London W4 4AL. Tel: 0181 996 7000. Fax: 0181 996 7001.

Title of publication	Principal regulations relevant	Comments
(BS = British Standard)		
International Electrotechnical Commission Publication 479. *Effects of current passing through the human body.* Parts I and II. Also published as BS PD 6519 Pts 1 and 2.	2	Definition of 'danger' and 'injury' - electric shock
International Electrotechnical Commission Guide 105. *Principles concerning the safety of equipment electrically connected to a tele-communications network.*	2	Ditto, on telecommunication systems
IEC 1201: 1992 *Extra-low voltage (ELV) limit values.* Also published as BS PD 6536: 1992	2	Electric shock - sets out limit values
The Institution of Electrical Engineers Regulations for Electrical Installations 16th Edition and associated guidance notes. (The IEE Wiring Regulations) (obtainable from the IEE, PO Box 96, Stevenage, Herts, SG1 2SD).	4(1) 5-12 inclusive	Selection of equipment and construction of installations up to 1000 volts ac. (Expected to be issued as BS 7671 during 1993)
BS 4363:1968. *Specification for distribution units for electricity supplies for construction and building sites.*	4, 6, 10	
BS 7375: 1991 *Distribution of electricity on construction and building sites.*	4, 6, 10	

Title of publication	Principal regulations relevant	Comments
BS 5486 Pt 1: 1990 (up to 1000 V ac and 1200 V dc) BS 5227: 1984 (above 1000 V ac and 1200 V dc)	4,5,12,15	Particular attention for switchgear clearance distances. Safety clearances and work sections
BS 6423:1983 *Code of practice for maintenance of electrical switchgear and control gear for voltages up to and including 650 V.*	4(2), 4(3), 12, 13	Precautions to secure safety of maintenance, personnel isolation procedures
BS 6626:1985 *Code of practice for maintenance of electrical switchgear and control gear for voltages above 650 V and up to and including 36 kV.*	4(2), 4(3), 12, 13	Precautions to secure safety of personnel
BS 6867: 1987 *Code of practice for maintenance of electrical switchgear and control gear for voltages above 36 kV*	4(2), 4(3), 12, 13	Ditto
BS EN 60204-1: 1993 *Electrical equipment of machines. Specification for general requirements,*	4,6	
BS 697:1986 *Specification for rubber gloves for electrical purposes.*	4(4), 14	
BS 921:1976 (1987) *Specification. Rubber mats for electrical purposes.*	4(4), 14	Mats for covering floor near electrical equipment where direct contact may occur
BS 5490:1977 (1985) *Specification for classification of degrees of protection provided by enclosures.*	6, 7	Index of Protection (IP) system against contact with live and moving parts and ingress of solids and moisture and Finger Test
BS 5420:1977 *Specification for degrees of protection of enclosures of switchgear and control gear for voltages up to and including 1000 V ac and 1200 V dc.*	6, 7	Ditto
BS 4999 Part 20:1972 *General requirements for rotating electrical machines. Classification of types of enclosure.*	6, 7	Index of Protection (IP) system against contact with live and moving parts and ingress of solids and moisture

Title of publication	Principal regulations relevant	Comments
BS 5345 *Code of practice for selection, installation and maintenance of electrical apparatus for use in potentially explosive atmospheres (other than mining applications or explosive processing and manufacture)*.	4(1), 4(2), 6	See also HSE booklet HSG22 (Appendix 1)
BS 5501 *Electrical apparatus for potentially explosive atmospheres*.	4(1), 6	See also HSE booklet HSG22 (Appendix 1)
BS CP 1003 *Electrical apparatus and associated equipment for use in explosive atmospheres of gas or vapour other than mining applications* (obsolescent, replaced by Parts 1 to 8 of BS 5345 but retained as a reference guide).	4(1), 4(2), 6	Ditto
BS 6742 Part 1:1987 *Electrostatic painting and finishing equipment using flammable materials. Specification for hand-held spray guns and associated apparatus.*	6	Protection against ignition
BS 6467: Part 1:1985 *Electrical apparatus with protection by enclosure for use in the presence of combustible dusts. Specification for apparatus.*	6	Ditto
BS 6467: Part 2: 1988 *Guide to selection, installation and maintenance.*	4, 5, 6	Ditto
BS 6651:1992 *Code of practice for protection of structures against lightning.*	6	As relevant to protection of electrical equipment from lightning
BS 5958: 1991 *Code of practice for control of undesirable static electricity.*	6	Precautions against ignition and electric shock
BS 4444:1969 (1980) *Guide to electrical earth monitoring.*	8	
BS 7430: 1991 *Earthing.*	8	

Title of publication	Principal regulations relevant	Comments
BS 5419:1977 (1990) *Specification for air break switches, air break disconnecters and fuse-combination units for voltages up to and including 1000V ac and 1200V dc.*	12	
BS 2754:1976 *Memorandum. Construction of electrical equipment for protection against electric shock.*	7, 8	
BS 5655:Part 1:1986 *Safety rules for the construction and installation of electric lifts.*	15	Clear areas in front of electric equipment specified (Clause 6.3.2.1)
BS 5253:1990 *Specification for AC disconnecters and earthing switches.* To be read in conjunction with BS 6581: 1985	12	

Working space and access; historical comment on revoked legislation (see regulation 15)

Among the legal provisions revoked upon the coming into force of the Electricity at Work Regulations 1989 were the Electricity (Factories Act) Special Regulations 1908 and 1944. Regulation 17 of those Regulations specified minimum width and height dimensions of 'switchboard passage-ways' if there were 'bare conductors' exposed or arranged to be exposed when 'live' so that they may be touched. These related to what are commonly known as 'open type' switchboards which had much exposed copper work, knife switches etc. That regulation (and the key definitions used at that time) are reproduced below for information. The dimensions which were specified by that regulation were arrived at after much consideration of the circumstances at the time. A compromise was struck between the objective of achieving the safety of those who had to work at and operate these 'open type' switchboards and the need to recognise the constraints imposed by the installations existing and the nature of the technology in 1908. Even though the dimensions were a compromise it was widely recognised that they were a good minimum standard which had been found necessary following a number of severe and fatal accidents in factories and power stations due to inadequate space or cluttered access in the vicinity of bare live conductors at these 'open type' switchboards. The dimensions chosen allowed workmen to operate or otherwise work upon the switchboard in reasonable safety and allowed, for example, persons to pass one another in the switchboard passageway without being placed at unacceptable risk of touching live conductors.

Where the need does arise to work on or near live conductors, the principles of providing adequate working space and uncluttered access/egress, which were expressed in regulation 17 of the Electricity (Factories Act) Special Regulations 1908 and 1944, should be given proper consideration.

Regulation 17 (of 1908 Regulations)

At the working platform of every switchboard and in every *switchboard passage-way*, if there be *bare conductors* exposed or arranged to be exposed when *live* so that they may be touched, there shall be a clear and unobstructed passage of ample width and height, with a firm and even floor. Adequate means of access, free from danger, shall be provided for every *switchboard passage-way*.

The following provisions shall apply to all such *switchboard* working platforms and *passage-ways* constructed after January 1, 1909 unless the *bare conductors*, whether overhead or at the sides of the *passage-ways*, are otherwise adequately protected against *danger* by divisions or screens or other suitable means:

(a)   Those constructed for *low pressure* and *medium pressure switchboards* shall have a clear height of not less than 7 ft and a clear width measured from *bare conductor* of not less than 3 ft.

(b)   Those constructed for *high pressure* and *extra high pressure switchboards*, other than operating desks or panels working solely at *low pressure*, shall have a clear height of not less than 8 ft and a clear width measured from *bare conductor* of not less than 3 ft 6 in.

(c)   *Bare conductors* shall not be exposed on both sides of the *switchboard passage*way unless either (i) the clear width of the passage is in the case of *low pressure* and *medium pressure* not less than 4 ft 6 in and in the case of *high pressure* and *extra high pressure* not less than 8 ft in each case measured between *bare conductors*, or (ii) the *conductors* on one side are so guarded that they cannot be accidentally touched.

Key definitions used in the 1908 Regulations

Switchboard means the collection of switches or fuses, *conductors*, and other *apparatus* in connection therewith, used for the purpose of controlling the current or pressure in any *system* or part of a *system*.

Switchboard passage-way means any passage-way or compartment large enough for a person to enter, and used in connection with a *switchboard* when *live*.

Low pressure means a *pressure* in a *system* normally not exceeding 250 volts where the electrical energy is used.

Medium pressure means a *pressure* in a system normally above 250 volts, but not exceeding 650 volts, where the electrical energy is used.

High pressure means a *pressure* in a *system* normally above 650 volts, but not exceeding 3000 volts, where the electrical energy is used or supplied.

Extra-high pressure means a *pressure* in a *system* normally exceeding 3000 volts where the electrical energy is used or supplied.

Printed and published by the Health and Safety Executive   C150   5/00